Young Le

CU00408648

Spotty Learns to Value Money

Sangita Koushik

© Young Learner Publications®, India

Spotty was the only child of her parents.
Her parents loved her very much and
fulfilled all her demands.

Whatever she wanted, she got. Her father even gave her pocket money to put in her money box.

Sadly, she did not save at all. Instead she spent all her money on ice creams, candies, toffees and what not!

One day, her father asked, "Spotty, how much money have you saved?"

Spotty replied, "Father, I only have a few coins in my money box."

Father was very upset with her. The next morning, he said to Spotty, "Get ready. We have to go somewhere."

Spotty asked, "Where are we going?"
Father replied, "Wait and watch." Soon,
they were on their way.

After a while, father stopped his car outside an old house. Spotty was surprised.

She saw many kids playing in the garden. As they entered the house, Spotty asked, "Father, what is this place?"

CHILDREN'S HOME

Father replied, "Spotty, not every child is lucky to have all that he or she wants. These children do not have parents, so they live here."

Spotty was surprised to hear this. She never knew of kids who could be alone in the world. She felt sad for the kids.

Then, father went up to a desk where a woman was sitting. He gave some money to her. Spotty asked her father, "What is this money for?"

12

Father replied, "She is Mrs. Kate. She looks after the children here. Many people help her in taking care of the kids by donating money."

13

At night, while in bed, Spotty thought, "I have been wasting money on useless things...